COMM 1500 Workbook

Department of Communication Studies

University of Georgia

Spring 2022

4750 Venture Drive, Suite 400
Ann Arbor, MI 48108
800-562-2147
www.xanedu.com

Author Note:

This workbook is the product of the work of multiple generations of faculty and graduate students in the Department of Communication Studies at the University of Georgia. The current edition was compiled and edited by Dr. Christin Huggins, Jessica Fabbricatore, and Allison Worsdale.

TABLE OF CONTENTS

Course Information

RESEARCH REQUIREMENT PROCESS

The Communication Studies Department requires all students taking COMM1110 and COMM1500 to satisfy a departmental research requirement. Students must earn research credit for each Communication Studies class that requires or offers research participation (e.g., students cannot use one research opportunity to apply to two classes). Students must earn 2 research credits per class to complete the research requirement.

The Research Requirement must be completed on or before Friday of Week 14 (i.e., the Friday before Reading Day). Failure to fulfill the research requirement by the due date will result in a grade of Incomplete (I). In order to remove the Incomplete (I), you must complete the research requirement in a future semester on SONA, noting the instructor is "from a previous semester," and then email that instructor.

Three research options are offered to fulfill this requirement. Students may complete any combination of the options to earn the 2 credits required.
- Option 1: Participation in a lab-based research study (2 credits)
- Option 2: Participation in an online study (1 credit)
- Option 3: Summarize a Communication research article (1 credit)

HOW TO ACCESS AVAILABLE RESEARCH OPPORTUNITIES:

Research opportunities will be posted regularly during the semester at: https://uga-comm.sona-systems.com. Once you are at this website, you need to (1) log into the system to view the list of available studies, (2) sign up for studies you are interested in and qualify for, and (3) track your progress throughout the semester. The system will also track when you receive credit for a study.

For new users: If you are a first-time user to the system, click the "***MyID login***" to authenticate your identity using your UGA MyID. On the next page, you will be able to request an account. You will be required to provide some basic information about yourself and your course information. After submitting the form, you will receive an email notification immediately.

A detailed instruction manual for using the system can be found here.
You can also watch video tutorial here: https://www.youtube.com/watch?v=_1OnT2ZU6QQ

Important: when signing up for a research opportunity, you *must* specify the correct instructor and course name for which the credit(s) should be assigned. If you don't see the instructor/course listed in SONA, contact commrp617@uga.edu.

OPTION 1:
PARTICIPATE IN A LAB-BASED COMMUNICATION RESEARCH STUDY
2 Credits
A **lab-based** research study involves you physically attending a scheduled research lab session in Caldwell Hall or other lab space on campus. The Department of Communication

Studies regards student participation in research studies as an educational experience for the participant, the researcher, and for the department. Student participation is appreciated and essential to the research of the Department of Communication Studies. Research contributions made by students are a lasting part of the body of social scientific knowledge about communication. The guidelines for research participation are as follows:

STEP 1: SIGN-UP FOR A <u>LAB-BASED</u> RESEARCH STUDY.

1.	Check the Communication Research Participation website regularly during the semester to look for studies: https://uga-comm.sona-systems.com
2.	When a study becomes available:
   a.	Make sure that you qualify to participate in the study (e.g., ensure that you meet all parameters set by the researcher or by the study).
   b.	Make sure it is **lab-based:** A lab-based research study involves you physically attending a scheduled research lab session in Caldwell Hall or other lab space on campus. Online research studies (i.e., completing an online survey from home) are described below.
3.	Sign-up (register for the study). Be sure to note what timeslot (session) you chose to participate, what will be expected of you, the approximate amount of time the study will take to complete, and the researcher's contact information.
4.	After signing up, you must participate in the research study to complete the research requirement.

STEP 2: PARTICIPATE IN THE LAB-BASED RESEARCH STUDY.

1.	Researchers may send you a follow-up e-mail to provide more detailed instructions. Make sure you follow the instructions provided in the email. You will also receive an automated email reminder of your study appointment the day before it is scheduled.
2.	*Because you are signing up for a study that requires you to physically attend a research lab*:
   a.	You must show up at the designated time and location.
   b.	When you show up for the study, please sign in using ***<u>both</u>*** your name <u>and</u> your instructor's name. The researchers need this information to ensure you receive participation credit for fulfilling the research requirement.
      1.	Note: If you must miss an appointment due to illness or emergency, please email the researcher and let him/her know.
3.	The researcher will grant you research credit through the online research participation system. You will receive a notification e-mail when you receive credit(s) for a study. Your instructor can view your credits through the research participation system as well.
4.	The researcher will grant you research credits as soon as possible, or within *48 hours of the study closing*, depending on their study needs. This means your credit may not be posted until weeks after you have participated in the study.
5.	If for some reason you do not receive credits for participating in a study, check with the researcher.
6.	Participation in a study must be completed **on or before Friday of Week 14 (i.e., the Friday before Reading Day.**

OPTION 2:
PARTICIPATE IN AN ONLINE COMMUNICATION RESEARCH STUDY
1 Credit

An **online** study is one that is completed at your own convenience via an emailed link to a research study. As noted above, student participation is appreciated and essential to the research of the Department of Communication Studies. The guidelines for research participation are as follows:

STEP 1: SIGN-UP FOR AN ONLINE RESEARCH STUDY.

1.   Check the Communication Research Participation website regularly during the semester to look for studies: https://uga-comm.sona-systems.com

2.   When a study becomes available:

    a.   Make sure that you qualify to participate in the study (e.g., ensure that you meet all parameters set by the researcher or by the study).

3.   Sign-up (register for the study). Be sure to note when the online survey link will expire, what will be expected of you, the approximate amount of time the study will take to complete, and the researcher's contact information.

4.   After signing up, you must participate in the online study to complete the research requirement.

STEP 2: PARTICIPATE IN THE ONLINE STUDY.

1.   Researchers may send you a follow-up e-mail to provide more detailed instructions. Make sure you follow the instructions provided in the email.

2.   If you sign up for an online study, *it is presumed that you will participate in the study shortly after you sign up for it*.

3.   The researcher will grant you research credit through the online research participation system. You will receive a notification e-mail when you receive credit(s) for a study. Your instructor can view your credits through the research participation system as well.

4.   The researcher will grant you research credits as soon as possible, or within *48 hours of the study closing*, depending on their study needs. This means your credit may not be posted until weeks after you have participated in the study.

5.   If for some reason you do not receive credit for participating in a study, check with the researcher.

6.   Participation in a study must be completed **on or before Friday of Week 14 (i.e., the Friday before Reading Day.**

OPTION 3:
SUMMARIZE A COMMUNICATION RESEARCH ARTICLE
1 Credit

This option allows students to read current research published in the Communication discipline. The objective is for students to read the article and apply it to their life experiences, thereby demonstrating the ability to understand the relevance of research in lived experience. This option will be available **from the beginning of the 13th week of the semester to the Friday before Reading Day**. Students must sign-up, select an article, and complete the option all through the SONA system. Guidelines for completion of the research article summary are as follows:

STEP 1: SIGN-UP TO SUMMARIZE A RESEARCH ARTICLE
1. Check the Communication Research Participation website beginning the 13th week of the semester to register to complete this option: https://uga-comm.sona-systems.com

STEP 2: SELECT ONE RESEARCH ARTICLE FROM OPTIONS ON SONA
1. Select ONE research article from the two options provided.
2. Read your chosen article at least two times.

STEP 3: COMPLETE QUESTIONS AND SUMMARY OF THE ARTICLE ON SONA
You MUST correctly answer the closed format questions AND submit a short essay applying the study findings to your own life experiences to earn credit for the research requirement. Failure to complete any portion of the below means you cannot pass the research requirement.
1. Answer closed format questions about the research article.
2. Write a short essay applying the findings of the study to your own life experience.
This short essay should have this structure:
1. State the generalization from the study you are focusing on
2. Describe the experience you believe is relevant to the generalization
3. Explain how it aligns with the study's results or complicates them
4. Offer any additional thoughts

Your essay should provide at least one unique, personal experience that illustrates or complicates the results of the study. For example, if the study indicates that self-disclosure of taboo information is more likely with strangers who you are not likely to meet again than with casual acquaintances, you might recount an incident when you told a stranger on a plane something that you had told no casual acquaintances. Or, complicating the study results, you might think of an instance when you told a casual acquaintance something you hadn't told anyone else, but explain why you think that this "taboo" subject did not seem forbidding to disclose to this person (or seemed desirable to disclose to this person).

1. The department will grant you research credit through the online research participation system. You will receive a notification e-mail when you receive credit(s) for a study. Your instructor can view your credits through the research participation system as well.

2. Completion of the summary of the research article must be done **on or before the Friday before Reading Day.**

3. If, after the Friday before Reading Day, you have not received credit for completing this assignment, check with the SONA director at commrp617@uga.edu.

Name: _____   Class time: _____

Syllabus, Research, and Academic Honesty Review

Directions: Answer the following questions from your Syllabus and Workbook

1.   Is the final exam cumulative? _____

        List the dates for the first, second, and third exams:

        Exam #1:_____   *Exam #2*:_____   *Exam #3*:_____

2.   Besides exams, what are the other two major assignments?

        1.

        2.

3.   Below are the specific course requirements for this class. How are the available

        points/percentages distributed?

        Exams = _____ *Points/Percent*

        Paper = _____ *Points/Percent*

        Group Project = _____ *Points/Percent*

        Participation= _____ *Points/Percent*

        Attendance = _____ *Points/Percent*

        Research Requirement = _____ *Points/Percent*

4.   What is the process to 1) discuss and 2) appeal a grade on an assignment or exam to the

        instructor?

        (1)

        (2)

6.   How is the late penalty assessed toward late assignments (deductions & timeframe)?

7.   When and where are your instructor's and/or GTA's office hours?

8. What are the three options (listed in the Communication Studies Workbook) available to fulfill your Communication Studies research requirement?

    (1) _____

    (2) _____

    (3) _____

9. Find the Communication Studies research portal at https://uga-comm.sona-systems.com.
    Are any current research opportunities available (write NO if not)? If so, what opportunities are posted?

***Answer the following questions from the* UGA's "A Culture of Honesty" (online)**

Paraphrase UGA's definition of Academic Honesty (in your own words).

In terms of conduct, is it necessary for a student to "intend" to violate the policy in order to be found in violation of the policy?
___Yes ___No

All students are required to be informed of the requirements in the "Culture of Honesty" Policy; therefore, lack of knowledge of the provisions is not an acceptable response to an allegation of dishonesty.
___True ___ False

What are the four major examples of Academic Dishonesty according to the UGA Culture of Honesty Policy?

1.

2.

3.

4.

I have read the COMM1500 Syllabus, Requirements for Communication Studies
Research Requirement and UGA Academic Honesty Policy and agree to abide by them:

Signature: _____ Date: _____

Name: _____   *Class time:* _____

Self and Peer Evaluation Form for Group Work

Directions: Write the name of each of your group members in a separate column. For each person (including yourself), indicate the extent to which you agree with the statement on the left, using the 1-5 scale below. Total the numbers in each column.

1= disagree strongly; 2=disagree somewhat; 3= neutral; 4=agree somewhat; 5=agree strongly

Evaluation Criteria	Self	Group member:	Group member:	Group member:	Group member:
Communicates effectively (about group meetings, division of labor, and role in project, etc.).					
Contributes meaningfully to group discussions					
Completes group assignments on time.					
Prepares work in a quality manner.					
Demonstrates a cooperative and supportive attitude.					
Contributes significantly to the project's success.					
TOTALS out of 30	/30	/30	/30	/30	/30

	Justifications for Evaluation Write one to two sentences justifying the scores you gave each person in the table above.
Self	
Group member:	
Group member:	
Group member:	
Group member:	

Name: _____   *Class time:* _____

Extra Credit: Attending a Public Speech

Directions: Please complete the following prompts for either the COMM Public Speaking Competition or the Georgia Debate Union's Russell Foundation Public Debate. You may only receive credit for one of these events. It is worth ½ of 1% of your final grade. This sheet must be completed and returned to your instructor within one week of the event.

Name of the event: _____

Date and location of the event _____

1. What are general strengths of the speakers? Provide a few specific examples in this paragraph connected to class concepts (use names of speakers).

2. What were areas of distraction or weakness in the speeches? Provide a few specific examples in this paragraph connected to class concepts (use names of speakers).

3. Identify a particular speaker and elaborate what drew you to this speaker (perhaps positively, perhaps negatively).

Course Activities

Name: _____   *Class time:* _____

1. Interpersonal Communication Competence Instrument

Objective: To assess your proficiency in each area of interpersonal communication competence and reflect on why certain areas are strengths or weaknesses.

Directions: Answer each item honestly as it currently applies to you in typical conversations with others. Use the below scale:

1= strongly disagree   2 = disagree   3 = undecided   4 = agree   5 = strongly agree

_____1.   I want to adjust the way I communicate with different people to best serve the conversation.

_____2.   I know how to adapt my behavior depending on the situation and with whom I'm interacting.

_____3.   I easily change how I communicate using a wide array of behaviors to benefit the interaction.

_____4.   I want to be actively engaged and paying attention in conversations.

_____5.   I know how to stay focused and attentive when interacting with others.

_____6.   I use a range of words and behaviors to show people I'm fully involved in conversations.

_____7.   I have a desire to control the direction of my interactions.

_____8.   I am aware of topic changes and know how to redirect conversations.

_____9.   I successfully manage the tone and flow of my interactions.

_____10.   I am motivated to understand what others are thinking and how they are feeling.

_____11.   I have the knowledge and experience needed to let others know I understand how they feel.

_____12.   I can communicate to others I share their emotional responses across a variety of contexts.

_____13.   I want to accomplish the goals I have for interactions.

_____14.   I know what to do and how to say things so that I achieve my interpersonal goals.

_____15.   When I want to gain something from a conversation, I can easily achieve my goals.

_____16.   I want to meet others' expectations of how I should act.

_____17.   I know the guidelines for how to act appropriately in most cases.

_____18.   I consistently act in ways that others consider to be appropriate.

=_____   /90 *Overall Total*

Scoring: Possible "Overall Total" should range between 18-90. Higher values indicate more communication competence.

Note: There are more scoring instructions on the back of this page that you must complete.

Six Criteria to Evaluate Interpersonal Communication Competence

Adaptability: Add your scores on items 1, 2, 3 = _____ /15
  These scores reflect your ability to change behaviors and goals to meet the needs of the interaction, also known as "flexibility".

Conversational Involvement: Add your scores on items 4, 5, 6 = _____ /15
  These scores reflect your ability to become cognitively engaged in the conversation and demonstrate engagement through interaction behaviors like head nods, vocal cues, etc.

Conversation Management: Add your scores on items 7, 8, 9 = _____ /15
  These scores reflect your ability to regulate conversation through controlling the topic, adjusting to a change in topic, interrupting, and asking questions.

Empathy: Add your scores on items 10, 11, 12 = _____ /15
  These scores reflect your ability to show your conversational partner that you understand his/her situation or that you share his/her emotional reactions to the situation.

Effectiveness: Add your scores on items 13, 14, 15 = _____ /15
  These scores reflect your ability to achieve the objectives you have for conversations.

Appropriateness: Add your scores on items 16, 17, 18 = _____ /15
  These scores reflect your ability to uphold the expectations for a given situation by behaving in ways other people expect of you. *Note: If you achieve your goals, but violate the expectations the other has for you and your relationship, then you are less than competent.*

In addition to examining your communicator competence, this scale allows you to examine your interpersonal communication motivation, knowledge and skills:

Motivation: Add your scores on items 1, 4, 7, 10, 13, and 16 = _____ /30
  This is your desire to approach or avoid conversation and/or social situations. Your goals (what you want and with whom) motivate you to act. Your confidence or lack of confidence that you will be successful affects your motivation, as well.

Knowledge: Add your scores on items 2, 5, 8, 11, 14, and 17 = _____ /30
  This involves knowing how to act. Once you decide to pursue a conversational goal, you construct plans to obtain it. Previous experience and/or observing others informs your knowledge of what constitutes a workable plan.

Skill: Add your scores on items 3, 6, 9, 12, 15, and 18 = _____ /30
  This involves the behaviors actually performed. You might be motivated and knowledgeable about how to act in the particular situation, but lack some basic skills.

Class Discussion Questions (be prepared to share answers in class):

1. Which areas did you score the highest in? Why do you think you scored higher in these areas?

2. Which areas did you score the lowest in? Why do you think you scored lower in these areas?

3. What are some ways in which you can improve on the areas you scored lower in?

Assessment items were created by Dr. Christin Huggins, while the structure was adapted from: Spitzberg, B. H. & Cupach, W. R. (1984). Interpersonal communication competence. Sage.

Name: _____   *Class time:* _____

2. Self-Concept Poem

Objective: *To illustrate your ideas of what makes up your self-concept and interpret how your understanding of self-concept can impact your interpersonal communication with others.*

Directions: Take 10-15 minutes to write a poem entitled "I am from." Each line must begin with the phrase "I am from…" You can include statements about where you are from regionally, ethnically, religiously, etc. The poem can include memories from different times in your life, interests or hobbies, mottos or credos, favorite places, family traditions/customs, or anything else you believe describes where you are from. Please be sure to include at least ten statements in your poem. Then, answer the questions that follow on the next page.

The following are some examples that may be of help:

I am from sliding around playing baseball on a snowy driveway.

I am from fish sticks, crinkle-cut frozen French fries and frozen mixes vegetables.

I am from primarily white, upper middle-class neighborhoods and racially diverse schools.

I am from diversity, multicultural education, identity, introspection, self-reflection, and social action.

I am from Tae Kwon Do, basketball, the batting cages, a soccer family and the gym.

I am from the History Channel, CNN, ESPN, Bravo and Home Team Sports.

I am from a wonderful family, close and loving and incredibly supportive.

"I Am From" poems are a commonly used pedagogy inspired by George Ella Lyon's poem, "Where I'm From."

Class Discussion Questions (be prepared to share answers in class):

Reviewing your poem, what does it say about your self-concept? What is important, what is unimportant, and how can you tell?

Reviewing your poem, do you think your self-esteem is generally positive or negative? What about your poem led you to your answer?

Which parts of your poem would be easier or harder to share with someone you just met? Why?

Name: _____   *Class time:* _____

3. Self-Disclosure Exercise

Objective*: To consider how self-disclosure works for a variety of topics and to analyze your levels of comfort with different types of disclosure.*

Directions: There are two parts to this activity. Part 1 is to be completed in groups. Part 2 is to be completed individually.

Part 1: Below are 7 questions that may challenge some of your attitudes, morals, values, and beliefs. Discuss these questions and your answers to them in groups of four or five individuals. You may skip questions or ask them out of order. You don't have to answer a question if you don't want to or are not comfortable doing so. Group members may not pressure anyone to answer the questions. You do NOT have to write down your answers to the questions in Part 1.

1. If you could have a superpower, what would it be?

2. Would you accept an offer of $1,000,00 if it required you to never speak to your family again?

3. If you could change anything about yourself such as a physical or personality trait, what would it be?

4. If you hear someone telling an offensive joke, do you speak up about it? Why or why not?

5. Would you like to be famous on social media? In what way?

6. If you could go back in time and give your younger-self advice, would you? What would the advice be?

7. Given the choice of anyone from history or the present, with whom would you want to have dinner?

Created by Huggins, Fabbricatore, & Worsdale, Fall 2021

Part 2: In the space below answer the following questions. You many continue your answers on a separate sheet of paper, if needed.

Class Discussion Questions (be prepared to share answers in class):
1. Which questions made you feel uncomfortable? Why?
2. Would you have answered these questions differently with your close friends? How so and why?
3. What kind of information did you disclose from each layer (peripheral, intermediate, central) of the social penetration model of self-disclosure? How did disclosing from each layer make you feel?

Self-Reflection Questions:
4. Were you always truthful? If you lied or did not answer, why?
5. Did any of your perceptions about the other group members change? Explain.
6. As a listener, are there certain topics you would rather not hear about from certain people?
7. What about this group of people made it harder to disclose to them? Easier?

Name: _____   *Class time:* _____

4. Johari Window

Objective: *To describe the types of information you disclose to others and understand how strength of relationships can determine what we disclose.*

Directions: Create a Johari Window for 1) your relationship with your instructor and 2)) your relationship with your best friend.

Give specific examples of the types of information you have disclosed or learned about yourself in each of the quadrants of the Window. You do not have to disclose personal information. You can give an example of the type of information you might disclose.

Instructor Johari Window

	Known to you	**Not known to you**
Known to others	*Public Area*	*Blind Area*
Not known to others	*Hidden Area*	*Unknown Area*

Best Friend Johari Window

	Known to you	Not known to you
Known to others	*Public Area*	*Blind Area*
Not known to others	*Hidden Area*	*Unknown Area*

Class Discussion Questions (be prepared to share answers in class):

1. How easy or difficult was it to select the information for each pane of the window? Why?

2. Regarding your Blind Area, what strengths might you possess that you don't recognize and how can you use these to strengthen your interpersonal communication? What flaws might you possess that you don't recognize and how can you improve on these?

3. What can you do to work towards unlocking the information described in your Unknown Area?

Name: _____   *Class time:* _____

5. First Impressions

Objective: *To identify influences on the perceptual process and understand how our own traits can impact our perceptions of others.*

Directions: Use the **two photos provided** to complete the worksheet below. You should make an informed guess about each individual for each question. Next to each response, give a brief justification for why you selected the answer you did. (ex: I guessed they are a policeman because of their uniform)

A   B

	Person A	Person B
Age:		
Career they have/desire to have:		
Relationship Status (single, dating, committed relationship):		
Where they grew up/what their hometown was like:		

	Person A	Person B
Liberal 1 2 3 4 5 Conservative		
Outgoing 1 2 3 4 5 Shy		
Partier 1 2 3 4 5 Workaholic		
Is this person religious?		
Where would this person go for fun?		
What kind of music would this person like?		
Any other thoughts about this person?		

Class Discussion Questions (be prepared to share answers in class):

1. To what extent do you feel your perceptions of each individual are accurate? What was your thought process behind your interpretations?

2. In what ways could your own sense of self impact your perceptions in the examples above?

Name: _____   *Class time:* _____

6. Forming Attributions

Objective: *To recognize the distinction between internal and external attributions and develop understanding of the different types of perceptual bias.*

Part 1:
Directions: For each scenario below, form an attribution (explanation) for the behavior, indicate whether it is an internal or an external attribution, and explain why.

1. **Example:** John stood up Jane on a date. John is picky about who he spends his time on and has been known to stand people up before. This is the first time Jane has been stood up.

   Attribution about John's behavior: *John is an inconsiderate person.*

   Circle one: (Internal)   External

   Explain: *John's character is the reason he stood Jane up because he has done this repeatedly. It's not external/situational (Jane's fault) because Jane hasn't been stood up before, so she wouldn't be the reason John stood her up.*

2. Tina just shared some very juicy and shocking gossip about Alex that she promised not to share. Tina is a quiet and introverted person who typically doesn't have a lot to say. Her friends were surprised to hear the gossip from Tina of all people.

   Attribution about Tina's behavior:

   Circle one: Internal   External

   Explain:

3. Haley is super nervous before giving a speech. She is typically an outgoing person who loves talking with people one-on-one or in small groups but last time Haley gave a speech, she almost threw up she was so nervous. The other two people on the podium who are giving speeches are acting nervous too.

   Attribution about Haley's behavior:

   Circle one: Internal   External

   Explain:

4. Eli had a really poor job interview. Afterwards he was annoyed with himself for forgetting about some really great examples he had of his work ethic. He also couldn't believe he forgot to rehearse a good answer for the question about what his "greatest weakness" might be. What kind of attribution is Eli making?

Attribution about Eli's behavior:

Circle one: Internal   External

Explain:

Part 2:
Directions: Create an interpersonal communication example for each of the following:

Fundamental attribution error:

Actor-observer effect:

Self-serving bias:

Class Discussion Questions on next page.

Class Discussion Questions (be prepared to share answers in class)**:**

1. What was the biggest challenge in identifying each example as an internal or external attribution?

2. What perceptual error(s) have you engaged in previously? What strategies can you employ to avoid engaging in these biases?

Name: _____ Class time: _____

7. Mock Interview

Objective: *To identify and interpret examples of internal and external attributions.*

Directions: Pair with a classmate to complete this activity. For this activity you will be completing a mock interview for an on-campus job or a position with an on-campus organization. One of you will be the interviewer and the other will be the applicant, then you will switch roles.

1. **Applicant Role - Name of the organization/position:**

2. **Interviewer Role – Name of the organization/position:**

As the Interviewer:

Ask 3 of the following questions:
- What do you consider to be your greatest weakness?
- What do you consider to be your greatest strength?
- How do you define success?
- Tell me about a time you made a mistake. What did you do to fix it?
- What are you passionate about?
- Why should we hire you over other qualified candidates?
- Where do you see yourself in 5 years?

Then answer the following questions in the space below:
1. What internal attributions did you make of the applicant? Was this positive or negative? Why?

2. What external attributions did you make of the applicant? Were these positive or negative? Why?

3. Would you hire this person for the position? Why or why not? Was your decision based on internal or external factors?

As the Applicant:
Answer the questions provided by your partner as you would in an interview setting. Then answer the following questions in the space below:

1. What internal attributions did you make of the interviewer? Was this positive or negative? Why?

2. What external attributions did you make of the interviewer? Were these positive or negative? Why?

3. Would you want to work for this person? Why or why not? Was your decision based on internal or external factors?

Name: _____ *Class time:* _____

8. Emotional Intelligence Assessment

Objective: *To identify your competence in each area of emotional intelligence and discover areas of strength and weakness.*

Directions: Emotional intelligence (referred to as EQ) is your ability to be aware of, understand and manage your emotions. Take the assessment below to identify your level of emotional intelligence using the scale below:

0	1	2	3	4
Not at all true of me		Neutral		Completely true of me

Self-Awareness of Emotion - *Total:*____

0 1 2 3 4	I can accurately label what I'm feeling when I am experiencing an emotion.
0 1 2 3 4	I can easily describe how I am feeling to others.
0 1 2 3 4	I clearly communicate how I feel the majority of the time.
0 1 2 3 4	I am rarely confused about how I feel.
0 1 2 3 4	I typically notice how I'm feeling each the day.
0 1 2 3 4	I can easily identify why I am feeling a certain way.

Empathy - *Total:*____

0 1 2 3 4	I'm good at accurately reading how other people are feeling.
0 1 2 3 4	I hurt when others hurt.
0 1 2 3 4	It's easy for me to put myself in someone else's shoes.
0 1 2 3 4	When someone tells me they are sad, it's easy for me to understand why they are sad.
0 1 2 3 4	I actively listen when people share with me how they are feeling.
0 1 2 3 4	When others tell me they are happy, I find myself feeling happy too.

Self-Regulation of Emotion - *Total:*____

0 1 2 3 4	I can easily calm myself down when I become upset.
0 1 2 3 4	I rarely feel out of control emotionally.
0 1 2 3 4	I often wait for an appropriate time to express my emotions.
0 1 2 3 4	When frustrated, I can change the way I think about the situation to help me feel better.
0 1 2 3 4	I almost never lose my temper.
0 1 2 3 4	I move on quickly when I'm unhappy; I don't dwell on the negative.

Continued on the next page.

Created by Dr. Christin Huggins, Fall 2021

Emotion Management in Communication - *Total:*____

0	1	2	3	4	
0	1	2	3	4	I am comfortable experiencing positive and negative emotions.
0	1	2	3	4	I express my emotions in ways that are helpful to my relationships.
0	1	2	3	4	I can tell others I am upset without hurting them in the process.
0	1	2	3	4	I use my emotions to help me think through my options when making decisions.
0	1	2	3	4	I can adjust my emotional responses to be constructive for the situation.
0	1	2	3	4	My emotions rarely prevent me from effectively communicating.

Key:

> **0 – 14 : Area for Enrichment**: Requires attention and development
>
> **15 – 20: Effective Functioning**: Consider strengthening
>
> **21 – 24: Enhanced Skills:** Use as leverage to develop weaker areas

Class Discussion Questions (be prepared to share answers in class):

1. What areas did you score the highest in? What areas did you score the lowest in? Why do you think you scored the way you did?

2. In what ways can you improve in the areas you scored the lowest?

3. What advice would you give to others that may have scored lower in the areas you excelled in?

Created by Dr. Christin Huggins, Fall 2021

Name: _____   *Class time:* _____

9. Emotion Diary

Objective: *To identify your emotions at various points in the day and examine how interpersonal communication impact the emotions we experience.*

An emotion is a strong reaction to an event that includes assessing event meaning, bodily responses, labeling the emotion experienced, regulating your reactions, and communicating the emotion experience both in word and action. An emotion is distinct from a feeling in that feelings are **short-term** emotional responses to events that yield **limited** arousal; we often do not try to manage feelings as we do emotions.

Directions: For one day, keep a diary of your emotions. Log your emotions at least 6 times. Be sure to keep in mind the definition of an emotion as you add to your diary. Try to be specific with the words you use to label your emotions, and be thoughtful when you reflect on what prompted each emotion. Once your diary is complete, answer the self-reflection questions.

Day completed:

1. Name of the emotion:

    Time of Day:

    What prompted this emotion?

2. Name of the emotion:

    Time of Day:

    What prompted this emotion?

3. Name of the emotion:

    Time of Day:

    What prompted this emotion?

4. Name of the emotion:

    Time of Day:

    What prompted this emotion?

5. Name of the emotion:

    Time of Day:

    What prompted this emotion?

6. Name of the emotion:

      Time of Day:

      What prompted this emotion?

Self-Reflection Questions (answer in the space provided below):

1. Did you struggle to identify your emotions for this activity? Why or why not?

2. In your opinion, how do interpersonal interactions impact your emotions?

3. In what ways do you try to manage your emotions?

Name: _____   *Class time:* _____

10. Tracking Feelings

Objective: *To illustrate the volatility of feelings and understand the forces that can influence our feelings.*

Directions: Watch Vernā Myers "How to overcome our biases? Walk boldly toward them" on TED.com. At the end of every 60 seconds during the TED talk, track your feelings with tally marks next to the corresponding feelings. You may feel more than one feeling at the end of each 60 second interval.

Positive Affect	Negative Affect
Attentive	Hostile
Active	Irritable
Alert	Ashamed
Excited	Guilty
Enthusiastic	Distressed
Determined	Upset
Inspired	Scared
Proud	Afraid
Interested	Jittery
Strong	Nervous

Afterward, record your answers to the following questions. Be prepared to discuss your answers in class.

1. Was it difficult to identify your feelings throughout? If so, why do you think that is?
2. Did you experience more positive or negative feelings? What feelings did you experience the most frequently? Why do you think that is?
3. How do you think your feelings throughout the TED Talk might compare to someone of a different race? Someone of a different gender? Someone from another country?

List of positive and negative feelings was taken from:
Watson, D., Clark, L. A., & Tellegen, A. (1988). Development and validation of brief measures of positive and negative affect: The PANAS scales. *Journal of Personality and Social Psychology, 54*(6), 1063-1070.

Name: _____   Class time: _____

11. Communication and Culture Field Work

Objective: *To define examples of co-cultures and interpret the factors that make up each co-culture.*

Directions: We experience Intercultural Communication every day. We may not always be aware of it, but it is occurring whether we are actively seeking out cultural activities or are just engaging in our everyday lives. **Choose 1 co-culture *that you belong to* then provide 3 *different examples* and/or symbols of the co-culture you chose.** In the sections below, (a) identify what culture group you selected– Who are its members? How are members identified? What is unique about this group? and (b) provide three examples of that co-culture including why you choose to focus on that particular example of your cultural group.

Co-culture Selected (that you belong to):

Example 1:

Example 2:

(Example 3 on next page)

Example 3:

Name: _____   *Class time:* _____

12. Elements of Sex Roles

Objective: *To identify your scores for the femininity and masculinity scales and reflect on how your results of the assessment are reflected in your interpersonal communication.*

Directions: Rate how TRUE each item is of you, using the following scale:

1	2	3	4	5	6	7
Never True	Almost Never True	Sometimes True	Undecided	Usually True	Almost Always True	Always True

1. ___ competitive
2. ___ affectionate
3. ___ loud
4. ___ athletic
5. ___ nurturing
6. ___ traditional
7. ___ courageous
8. ___ takes care of others
9. ___ indecisive
10. ___ considered a leader
11. ___ compassionate
12. ___ boisterous
13. ___ risk-taker
14. ___ empathetic
15. ___ calm
16. ___ self-seeking
17. ___ accessorize your things
18. ___ curious
19. ___ adventurous
20. ___ enjoy baking
21. ___ divisive
22. ___ masculine
23. ___ caring
24. ___ self-conscious
25. ___ enjoy hunting
26. ___ sensitive
27. ___ shy

28. ___ protective
29. ___ enjoy cooking
30. ___ inquisitive
31. ___ use profanity
32. ___ concerned with skincare
33. ___ sociable
34. ___ enjoy playing videogames
35. ___ submissive
36. ___ thoughtful
37. ___ ambitious
38. ___ emotional
39. ___ uncertain
40. ___ rational
41. ___ collaborative
42. ___ quiet
43. ___ likes time outdoors
44. ___ enjoy time with children
45. ___ cautious
46. ___ assertive
47. ___ organized
48. ___ talkative
49. ___ willing to defend others
50. ___ loyal
51. ___ introspective
52. ___ logical
53. ___ feminine
54. ___ outgoing

(Scoring on back)

Characteristics selected are original to the authors of this workbook. Inventory structure adapted from: Bem, S. L. (1981). *Bem Sex-Role Inventory: Professional manual*. Palo Alto: Consulting Psychologists Press.

Scoring:

Masculinity score: Add up your ratings for items 1, 4, 7, 10, 13, 16, 19, 22, 25, 28, 31, 34, 37, 40, 43, 46, 49, and 52. Divide the total by 18. _____

Femininity score: Add up your ratings for items 2, 5, 8, 11, 14, 17, 20, 23, 26, 29, 32, 35, 38, 41, 44, 47, 50, and 53. Divide the total by 18. _____

If your masculinity score is above 4.9 (the approximate median for the masculinity scale) and your femininity score is above 4.9 (the approximate femininity median), then you would be classified as androgynous on the scale.

Self-Reflection Questions:
Were there some words you thought were true of yourself, but wished were not true? What were these words?

Words you didn't think were true of yourself, but wished were true? What were these words?

Do you agree with the way the items are divided into masculinity and femininity? Would you delete, add, or switch any items in the categories?

How do you feel about your score? Are you surprised? Why or why not?

What factors did you consider when scoring yourself? (Your self-concept? What your family and friends think? Be specific and use course concepts.)

Characteristics selected are original to the authors of this workbook. Inventory structure adapted from: Bem, S. L. (1981). *Bem Sex-Role Inventory: Professional manual*. Palo Alto: Consulting Psychologists Press.

Name: _____   *Class time:* _____

13. Listening Diary

Objective: *To identify successful and unsuccessful listening techniques used throughout the day and reflect on your listening strengths and weaknesses.*

Directions: Throughout the day, pay attention to and log three different listening interactions using this listening diary. Specifically, pay attention to how you listened actively, what function you were listening for, and what forms of incompetent listening you may have been engaging in. At the end of the day, reflect on your experiences and develop a plan for future improvement.

Day Completed:

Interaction #1:

Who you were listening to: _____

Active listening techniques: _____

Listening function: _____

Incompetent listening: _____

Interaction #2:

Who you were listening to: _____

Active listening techniques: _____

Listening function: _____

Incompetent listening: _____

Interaction #3:

Who you were listening to: _____

Active listening techniques: _____

Listening function: _____

Incompetent listening: _____

Self-Reflection Questions:

What were your biggest issues in listening throughout the day?

What are some possible areas for improvement?

Develop a plan to engage in better active listening in the future:

Name: _____ *Class time:* _____

14. Cooperative Communication

Objective: *To identify the four criteria of the Cooperative Principle and discover how uncooperative communication can impact a conversation and relationship.*

Directions: Reflect on a time when someone who communicated with you was not cooperative (in other words, they didn't help you advance the conversation). How could you tell they were not being cooperative? How did it make you feel? Write a one-page reflection answering these prompts. Include and underline the four criteria of the Cooperative Principle (informative, honest, relevant, clear) in your reflection.

Name: _____   *Class time:* _____

15. Personal Report of Communication Apprehension

Objective*: To discover your level of communication apprehension in different communication contexts and explain how this knowledge might help you in future interpersonal interactions.*

Directions: This instrument is composed of 24 statements concerning feelings about communicating with other people. Please indicate the degree to which each statement applies to you using the following scale:

1= strongly agree   2 = agree   3 = undecided   4 = disagree   5 = strongly disagree

___ 1. I dislike participating in group discussions.

___ 2. I am generally comfortable while participating in group discussions.

___ 3. I am tense and nervous while participating in group discussions.

___ 4. I like to get involved in group discussions.

___ 5. Engaging in group discussions with new people makes me tense and nervous.

___ 6. I am calm and relaxed while participating in group discussions.

___ 7. Generally, I am nervous when I have to participate in a meeting.

___ 8. Usually, I am calm and relaxed while participating in a meeting.

___ 9. I am calm and relaxed when called upon to express an opinion at a meeting.

___ 10. I am afraid to express myself at meetings.

___ 11. Communicating at meetings usually makes me feel uncomfortable.

___ 12. I am relaxed when answering questions at a meeting.

___ 13. While participating in a conversation with a new acquaintance I feel very nervous.

___ 14. I have no fear of speaking up in conversations.

___ 15. Ordinarily, I am very tense and nervous in conversations.

___ 16. Ordinarily I am calm and relaxed in conversations.

___ 17. While conversing with a new acquaintance I feel very relaxed.

___ 18. I am afraid to speak up in conversations.

___ 19. I have no fear of giving a speech.

___ 20. Certain parts of my body feel tense and rigid while giving a speech.

___ 21. I feel relaxed while giving a speech.

___ 22. My thoughts become confused and jumbled when giving a speech.

___ 23. I face the prospect of giving a speech with confidence.

___ 24. When giving a speech, I am so nervous I forget facts I really know.

Obtained from: http://www.jamescmccroskey.com/measures/prca24.htm.
Original Source: McCroskey, J. C. (1982). An introduction to rhetorical communication (4th Ed).
Englewood Cliffs, NJ: Prentice-Hall. Source states permission for open use (7/14/2021).

Scoring Instructions:

Part 1: Calculate scores

For each section below, **begin with a score of 18 points.** Then add and subtract your own scores from that starting score of 18 points. For example, let's say you scored a 3 on all items. To determine your group discussion score you would complete the following: 18 + (sum of score on items 2, 4, and 6) – (sum of score on items 1, 3, and 5), which would be 18 + 9 – 9 = 18.

Group Discussions: Begin with a score of 18, then add your scores for items 2, 4, and 6. Then subtract your scores for items 1, 3, and 5. TOTAL: _____

Meetings: Begin with a score of 18, then add your scores for items 8, 9, and 12. Then subtract your scores for items 7, 10, and 11. TOTAL: _____

Interpersonal Conversation: Begin with a score of 18, then add your scores for items 14, 16, and 17. Then subtract your scores for items 13, 15, & 18. TOTAL: _____

Public Speaking: Begin with a score of 18, then add your scores for items 19, 21, and 23. Then subtract your scores for items 20, 22, and 24. TOTAL: _____

Part 2: Re-enter your scores* for each type of communication below:
Group Discussion score _____

Meetings score _____

Interpersonal Conversation score _____

Public Speaking score _____

> *Scores on each of four types of communication above (groups, meetings, interpersonal conversations, and public speaking) can range from 6 to 30. Higher scores indicate higher levels of discomfort or apprehension.*

Part 3: Sum your scores for the four types of communication above to determine your total communication apprehension score.

TOTAL Communication Apprehension score: _____

> *Your total communication apprehension score should be between 24 and 120. Higher scores indicate higher levels of discomfort or apprehension.*

Part 4: Compare your scores with the Norms for PRCA:

Context	Average Score	Average Range	High Apprehension Scores
Group	15.4	11 to 20	21 & Above
Meetings	16.4	13 to 20	21 & Above
Interpersonal	14.2	11 to 18	19 & Above
Public Speaking	19.3	14 to 24	25 & Above
Overall	65.6	51 to 80	81 & Above

Class Discussion Questions (be prepared to share answers in class):

Which of these scores do you think COMM 1500 will help you with? Explain why.

Are your scores what you expected? Why or why not?

How would the strategy of a communication plan help in these situations? What other strategies might be useful?

Name: _____   *Class time:* _____

16. Nonverbal Communication

Objective: *To identify various nonverbal communication behaviors from everyday life and describe how they differ depending on relationship type.*

Directions: Select 3 out of 4 relationship types (romantic, friendship, family, and workplace) and then describe the following nonverbals within each of the three relationship types you selected. Think about the different levels of intimacy and how that might impact what nonverbals you would use. (For this activity, think about the "How's it going? How's your day?" small talk conversations or greeting another person.)

- Body/face orientation
- Facial expressions
- Touch
- Gestures
- Space/Physical proximity
- Eye contact/gaze
- Environment/relevant artifacts

Romantic Relationships

Friendship Relationships

Family Relationships

Workplace Relationships

Class Discussion Questions (be prepared to share answers in class):
Nonverbal communication can convey the closeness and power in a relationship (among other things).
How is your nonverbal communication different across different relationships?

Does your nonverbal communication stay the same across all relationships?

Can you think of a time when unintentionally communicated something through nonverbal communication?

Name: _____   *Class time:* _____

17. Observing Nonverbals Across Cultures

Objective: *To compare and contrast nonverbal communication across cultures.*

Directions: Think of a culture you have visited or would like to visit in the future. Try to pick a culture that differs a lot from the U. S. Using the Internet, answer the following questions:

1. Identify the nonverbal gestures that are frequently used in this culture, but that you aren't familiar with in your own cultures? What are their range of meanings?

2. Describe how people in this culture use gaze. Consider directness of eye contact, places where people do not seem to direct their gaze, and differences among different groups of people.

3. What range of clothing styles do you notice? Do there appear to be rules or norms about when particular styles are worn and who should wear them (or not wear them)?

4. What appear to be the customs related to the use of space? Do some people occupy or control more space than others? Are different kinds of communication held with different spacing? Are there distinctive elements that mark off space?

5. Now, select one group of people (such as children, men, police officers, low income individuals). Then compare and contrast the nonverbal behavior of that group within the culture you selected and another cultural group with which you are familiar. Where are the similarities between the two cultures the greatest for this group of people? Where do the differences between the two cultures appear to be the greatest?

* Questions by workbook team, after the general orientation in Solomon, D., & Theiss, J. (2013). *Interpersonal communication : Putting theory into practice*. ProQuest Ebook Central https://ebookcentral.proquest.com

Name: _____   *Class time:* _____

18. Nonverbal Communication Codes

Objective: *To identify everyday use of nonverbal communication codes in interpersonal settings.*

Directions: Select a situation to observe an interaction(s) in your daily life. For example, you may choose to observe your roommates talking with one another or a group of your friends at dinner. During the observed interaction, find an example of each of the nonverbal communication codes listed below.

1.   **Kinesics**
     - Facial expression
     - Eye contact
     - Gestures (emblems, illustrators, regulators, adaptors)

2.   **Haptics**
     - Look for examples of these types of touch: Functional-professional, Social-polite, Friendship-warmth, Love-intimacy

3.   **Proxemics**
     - Look for examples of the four communication distances (intimate, personal, social, and public space)
     - Look for examples of territoriality

Continued on the next page.

4. **Physical appearance**
   - Look for examples of how someone may be trying to communicate through their clothing choices.

5. **Artifacts**
   - Look for examples of at least five artifacts and indicate what they communicate to you.

6. **Environment -**
   - Describe the *fixed* features of the environment. Be specific.
   - Describe the *semifixed* features of the environment. Be specific.

Self-Reflection Question:
Given your observations, how you think that the location and/or relationship types influenced the nonverbal codes used?

Name: _____   *Class time:* _____

19. Conflict Mode Assessment

Objective: *To determine your communicative approaches to conflict and speculate how your approach may change based on different interpersonal situations.*

Directions: Consider situations in which you find your wishes/goals differing from those of another person. Respond to each statement by circling how much you agree or disagree with it as it applies to how you would typically react to a disagreement.

1= strongly disagree   2 = disagree   3 = undecided   4 = agree   5 = strongly agree

1. I seek to achieve my preferred outcome by whatever means necessary 1   2   3   4   5

2. I work with the other person to come up with a creative solution that works

    for both of us...1   2   3   4   5

3. I'm willing to give up something if the other person is willing to give up

    something as well 1   2   3   4   5

4. When my wishes differ from others, I keep those topics to myself 1   2   3   4   5

5. I focus on the other person's feelings when solving problems...........................1   2   3   4   5

6. I make sure to get my points across..1   2   3   4   5

7. I ask for and encourage the other person to help me solve the issue..................1   2   3   4   5

8. I work to find equal amounts of wins and losses for each of us 1   2   3   4   5

9. I tend to put off talking about disagreements 1   2   3   4   5

10. I try to keep other from being hurt 1   2   3   4   5

11. I convince the other person that the only correct solution is my solution........1   2   3   4   5

12. I encourage others to talk so that we can develop new solutions 1   2   3   4   5

13. I often suggest meeting in the middle to solve problems 1   2   3   4   5

14. I do my best to avoid talking about disagreements 1   2   3   4   5

15. I defer to what the other person wants to do..1   2   3   4   5

16. I often overpower the other person with reasons why I'm right 1   2   3   4   5

17. I seek to find a solution that satisfies all aspects of each party's concerns 1   2   3   4   5

18. I let go of some of what I want, if the other person does the same 1   2   3   4   5

19. I often think it's not worth it to bring up issues that could cause tension 1   2   3   4   5

20. I view achieving the other person's desires as more important than achieving

    my own 1   2   3   4   5

Created by Dr. Christin Huggins, Fall 2021

21. I do my best to win arguments..1   2   3   4   5

22. I come together with others so that we all get what we want 1   2   3   4   5

23. I suggest a solution that includes portions of each party's solution 1   2   3   4   5

24. I hint about things that bother me without saying something directly 1   2   3   4   5

25. I often give up what I want, so that the other person achieves their goals 1   2   3   4   5

26. I tend to dominate the conversation when discussing disagreements 1   2   3   4   5

27. I openly share my viewpoint, and ask the other person to share theirs 1   2   3   4   5

28. I typically work to split the difference between the two parties' ideas 1   2   3   4   5

29. I prefer to just let things go rather than bring them up 1   2   3   4   5

30. I think the best solutions are the ones that make the other person happy.........1   2   3   4   5

Scoring is on the next page.

Created by Dr. Christin Huggins, Fall 2021

Scoring Instructions

Part 1: Calculate scores

Competing: Add your scores for items 1, 6, 11, 16, 21, and 26. TOTAL: _____
Competition is high in assertiveness and low in cooperation seeking to force others to bend to their solution to the problem.

Collaborating: Add your scores for items 2, 7, 12, 17, 22, and 27. TOTAL: _____
Collaborating is high in assertiveness and high in cooperation seeking to develop new, creative solutions to problems that are mutually determined.

Compromising: Add your scores for items 3, 8, 13, 18, 23, and 28. TOTAL: _____
Compromising is moderate in assertiveness and moderate in cooperation seeking find the middle ground between two viewpoints without generating a new solution.

Avoiding: Add your scores for items 4, 9, 14, 19, 24, and 29. TOTAL: _____
Avoidance is low in assertiveness and low in cooperation work to deny the existence of the conflict to both self and others.

Accommodating: Add your scores for items 5, 10, 15, 20, 25, and 30. TOTAL: _____
Accommodating is low in assertiveness and high in cooperation focusing on meeting the needs of others without putting forward one's own desires for resolving the issue.

Part 2: KEY

Minimum Score: 6
Median Score: 18
Maximum Score 30

Class Discussion Questions (be prepared to share answers in class):

- What was your highest score? Give an example of how you use your primary conflict mode (highest score) in interpersonal communication. For instance, what is a specific example of a time when you avoided, compromised, collaborated, competed, or accommodated in conflict)?

- What are the short- and long-term interpersonal effects of using this conflict mode?

- What was your lowest conflict mode? Can you think of a time when you have used that conflict mode? How did that conflict end?

Created by Dr. Christin Huggins, Fall 2021

Name: _____   Class time: _____

20. Power Inventory

Objective: *To recognize your power currencies and reflect on how those currencies might be beneficial or detrimental to interpersonal communication and relationships.*

Directions: For each type of power currency, make a list of the sources of power you think you have. Try to get at least **three** sources of power in each category. Be creative and thoughtful as you reflect on your power in interpersonal relationships.

Resource Currency: (*ex: the money my internship pays me*)

Expertise Currency: (*ex: the classes I've taken so far in college*)

Social Network Currency: (*ex: the people I play Dungeons and Dragons with*)

Personal Currency: (*ex: my sense of humor*)

Intimacy Currency: (*ex: my relationship with _____ is very close*)

Self-Reflection Questions on the next page.

Self-Reflection Questions:

- In your opinion, what is *your* most beneficial power currency in interpersonal communication? Why? How has this power currency benefited you in the past?

- What is *your* least beneficial power currency in interpersonal communication? Why? How might you acquire more power currency in that area?

Name: _____ *Class time:* _____

21. Songs for the Relationship Cycle

Objective: *To demonstrate your understanding of and distinctions among Knapp's stages of coming together and coming apart through pop culture references.*

Directions: Below are the stages of the relational development model. Provide an example of a song *lyric* that illustrates each of the stages. **Include the song title, artist, and song lyric in each response.** <u>Note</u>: If you can't think of a song lyric, you can use quotes from a book or lines from a movie.

Coming Together Stages

INITIATING - goal is to show that you are interested in making contact and to show the other person that you are worth talking to. "Hi, how are you?" "Fine. You?"

Song title & artist: _____

Lyric: _____

EXPERIMENTING - contact is made and you begin the search for common ground. "Where are you from?" "What classes are you taking?"

Song title & artist: _____

Lyric: _____

INTENSIFYING - feelings are expressed directly. Metacommunication, or communication about how they communicate, about the state of the relationship occurs. Spending a great deal of time together, provision of social support, and proof of commitment. "I think I love you." "I love you too."

Song title & artist: _____

Lyric: _____

INTEGRATING - individuals begin to take on an identity as a social unit. They become a "WE" and take on each other's commitments. "ME" is somewhat de-emphasized. "We like to go there!" "Yeah, we are like one person." "What happens to you happens to me"

Song title & artist: _____

Lyric: _____

BONDING - symbolic and *formal public gestures* are made to show the world that their relationship exists (i.e. marriage license, wedding rings). Relational commitment is evident and central for both partners.

Song title & artist: _____

Lyric: _____

Coming Apart Stages

DIFFERNTIATING – beliefs, attitudes and values that distinguish you from your partner come to dominate your thoughts and communication. Differences are exploited, partners become more individualistic. "I can't believe you of all people think that!"

Song title & artist: _____

Lyric: _____

CIRCUMSCRIBING- Primary focus shifts from differences to setting limits and boundaries on communication between the two people. The communication becomes much shallower and the range of topics significantly decline. Partners may fear discussing deep topics because of the threat of a conflict, leading to less communication altogether. "Let's not talk about that anymore." "We always fight when we talk about your mom; let's not talk about her anymore."

Song title & artist: _____

Lyric: _____

STAGNATION-- Builds off many of the problems of the circumscribing stage; communication becomes more limited and less frequent. It seems like no topic is really safe anymore. Stagnating relationships do not grow or progress but rather invoke a feeling of "nothing changes". "I feel claustrophobic" "I feel trapped."

Song title & artist: _____

Lyric: _____

AVOIDANCE--This stage takes the limited communication to a physical level. Partners may avoid each other altogether, desiring separation from one another. "I don't want to see you anymore." Ignoring texts from your partner.

Song title & artist: _____

Lyric: _____

TERMINATION-- Break up. People talk about how to break up (so, who gets the dog?). They might talk about the past/present/future of the relationship. "I'll never find a person as perfect as you." "I can't believe you cheated on me!"

Song title & artist: _____

Lyric: _____

Class Discussion Questions (be prepared to share answers in class):

Thinking of the romantic relationships you have seen or been a part of, do you feel like most relationships conform to or defy Knapp's stages? Why?

Name: _____   Class time: _____

22. Attachment Styles

Objective: *To identify your own attachment style and explore how that attachment style influences your communication with romantic partners.*

Directions: This activity includes two parts. You will: 1) complete the measure of romantic relationship attachment. 2) on the next page, calculate your scores to determine your attachment style.

Part 1: *Complete the following measure.* Think about a current or a recent romantic relationship and respond to each statement by circling how much you agree or disagree with it. If you haven't had a romantic relationship, envision how you think you might feel/act. Use the following scale:

1= strongly disagree   2 = disagree   3 = undecided   4 = agree   5 = strongly agree

1. Being connected to my romantic partner is important to me 1   2   3   4   5

2. I often worry that my partner's feelings for me will change 1   2   3   4   5

3. It's easy for me to be vulnerable and self-disclose to my partner 1   2   3   4   5

4. It makes me nervous to spend time away from my partner................................1   2   3   4   5

5. I am comfortable being emotionally close to my partner...................................1   2   3   4   5

6. I often worry that my partner is going to leave me 1   2   3   4   5

7. I tend to feel insecure when I'm not in a romantic relationship 1   2   3   4   5

8. I'm concerned that I may be single forever 1   2   3   4   5

9. I rarely want to take a step back in my romantic relationships 1   2   3   4   5

10. I have a tendency to become clingy in romantic relationships.........................1   2   3   4   5

11. I'm totally comfortable with my partner opening up to me 1   2   3   4   5

12. I often wonder if my partner feels for me the way I feel about them 1   2   3   4   5

13. I rarely desire emotional distance from my partner...1   2   3   4   5

14. In relationships, I tend to push my partner toward commitment......................1   2   3   4   5

All statements were created by Dr. Christin Huggins, Fall 2021. Instrument structure was adapted from: Wei, M., Russell, D. W., Mallinckrodt, B., & Vogel, D. L. (2007). The experiences in close relationship scale (ECR)-short form: Reliability, validity, and factor structure. *Journal of Personality Assessment, 88*(22), 187-204. DOI: 10.1080/00223890701268041

Part 2: *Determine Your Attachment Style*

1. Add up your scores on the Odd numbered questions and divide by 7. This is your score for **Relationship Avoidance.** If your score is greater or equal to 3.5, you are low on Relationship Avoidance. If your score is less than 3.5, you are high on Relationship Avoidance. **Avoidance Score** _____ high / low

2. Add up your scores on the Even numbered questions and divide by 7. This is your score for **Anxiety Over Relationships.** If your score is greater or equal to 3.5, you are high on Anxiety Over Relationships. If your score is less than 3.5, you are low on Anxiety Over Relationships. **Anxiety Score**_____ high / low

The Attachment Style Dimensions Translate to the Following Attachment Categories:

_____ *Secure*: Low on avoidance, low on anxiety
_____ *Preoccupied*: Low to Average on avoidance, high on anxiety
_____ *Dismissive:* High on avoidance, low on anxiety
_____ *Fearful*: High on avoidance, high on anxiety

Self-Reflection Question:

Write ways in which it might be difficult or easy for a person with your attachment style to communicate with or be in relationship with a person for each other attachment style. For example, how would a dismissive style be able to communicate with a secure attachment style?

Secure:

Preoccupied:

Dismissive:

Fearful:

Name: _____   Class time: _____

23. Revised Family Communication Pattern Instrument

Objective: *To identify your family's communication pattern and reflect on how that communication pattern influences how you communicate with others in various settings.*

Directions: To complete this instrument, you will need to login to the eLC page for your section of COMM1500. Your instructor will provide course specific instructions for accessing the measure. The Revised Family Communication Patterns Activity on eLC will include the specific directions for completing the instrument. Please answer all questions with one family unit in mind. Once you complete the measure, use this workbook page to calculate your scores and determine your family type.

The Revised Family Communication Pattern Instrument measures two dimensions of family communication: conversation orientation and conformity orientation.

Scoring:

Conversation Orientation

Sum the number of items you agreed with for conversation orientation

       Score: _____/15   circle: low / high

     ➤ 6 on Conversation is high

Conformity Orientation

Sum the number of items you agreed with for conformity orientation

       Score: _____/11   circle: low / high

     ➤ 5 on Conformity is considered high

Family Type: Select the family type below that corresponds to your scores on the conversation and conformity orientations.

        Consensual: High conversation/High conformity
        Pluralistic: High conversation/low conformity
        Protective: Low conversation/High conformity
        Laissez-faire: Low conversation/Low conformity

       My family type _____

Self-Reflection Questions on the next page

Created by Huggins, Fabbricatore, & Worsdale, Fall 2021

Self-Reflection Questions:
Considering your family communication pattern:
- How has your family pattern changed over time?
- What aspects of your family communication pattern do you hope to continue using in your own future family? Why?
- What aspects of your family communication pattern would you change in your own future family?

Created by Huggins, Fabbricatore, & Worsdale, Fall 2021

Name: _____ *Class time:* _____

24. Long-distance Friendship Maintenance

Objective: *To identify ways to maintain friendships when facing the challenge of being separated by distance that can be implemented in current and future friendships*

Directions: Friendships face a variety of challenges, but geographic separation is the most common. Working on your own or with a partner, develop a communication plan for maintaining a current long-distance friendship. Then, identify how your plan will be successful in the short-term and long-term.

Part 1: Develop a Communication Plan
Consider addressing the following:
- How often will you communicate?
- What media will you use?
- What topics will you discuss?
- What rules might you develop for your communication?

Part 2: Identify Relationship Outcomes
Identify the possible short-term and long-term effects of your plan? What positives do you anticipate? Are there any negatives that could result?

Part 3: Self-Reflection Question
Think of a time in the past that you used one of the strategies outlined in your communication plan? How did this strategy help/hurt your friendship?

Created by Huggins, Fabbricatore, & Worsdale, Fall 2021

COMM1500 Workbook, page 76

Name: _____   Class time: _____

25. Upward and Downward Communication

Objective: *To reflect on communication in a previous workplace relationship in an effort to identify ways to implement effective upward and downward communication in the future.*

Directions: Reflect on a supervisory relationship you have had in the past. This relationship could be with a boss, a teacher, a mentor, a coach, etc. Consider the ways in which your supervisor communicated downward to you and how you communicated upward to them. Finally, consider how you will use these experiences in your own future downward communication.

Supervisory relationship for reflection: _____

Part 1: Upward Communication

Describe some characteristics of your communication with your supervisor:

Did you ever engage in advocacy with your supervisor? Why or why not? If so, how?

Part 2: Downward Communication

Describe how your supervisor was competent or incompetent in communicating with you?

How did your supervisor compliment or criticize you? How did this affect you?

Self-Reflection Questions on the next page.

Self-Reflection Questions:

What elements of the communication between you and supervisor did you like and dislike?

How can you improve in your own upward communication in the future?

How will you use this supervisory relationship experience to affect how you will communicate downward in your potential future positions as a supervisor?

Name: _____   *Class time:* _____

26. APA Style Activity

Objective*: To familiarize yourself with a common formatting and citation style for social sciences. To prepare you to correctly format assignments for COMM 1500 and other social science courses.*

Directions: Follow the instructions for each item. Type your responses, staple the pages together, and turn them in on the due date: _____.

Note: **You should ONLY use the workbook for this activity AND for your class paper.** Do not use online APA style suggestions as they may conflict with the workbook. If your formatting conflicts with the workbook, you will lose points on your assignments.

Using only the workbook:

1.　Construct an appropriate APA Style title page for the following student paper:
　　　Finding Strength in Weakness: Navigating Gaslighting's Challenges to Intimacy Power. Written by Lee M. Pierce for Dr. Monahan's Spring 2015 COMM 1500 class, 10:00 section.

2.　Use the sentence below from Chapter One, p. 14, in your textbook. Cut and paste the sentence into your document and do the following (1) show how you cite the sentence as a direct quotation (2) write the sentence, including the citation.
　　　"Finally, you use interpersonal communication to achieve relationship goals – building, maintaining, or terminating bonds with others."

3.　Use the sentence below from Chapter One, p. 14, in your textbook. Type this sentence into your document and show how you properly cite the author of this idea (Maslow) as a secondary source.
　　　"At the foundational level are physical needs such as air, food, water, sleep, and shelter."

4.　*Paraphrase* the sentence below and cite it properly. This is from p. 246 in your textbook.
　　　"A final way in which we communicate nonverbally is through our environment, the physical features of our surroundings."

5.　Cite the following YouTube video:
　　　"Amy Cuddy TED Talk – Fake it Till You Make It" posted by Sara Moore on July 8, 2016 at https://youtu.be/RVmMeMcGc0Y

6.　Create a Reference page for the following 3 sources:

- Appearance-related communication and body image outcomes: Fat talk and old talk among mothers and daughters. By Dr. Analisa Arroyo and Kristen K. Andersen. Journal of Family Communication. 2016, Vol. 16, p. 95-110.

- Reflect & Relate: An Introduction to Interpersonal Communication. By: Steven McCornack and Kelly Morrison. 5th edition. 2019. Bedford/St. Martin's.

- Revised third edition of the COMM1500 workbook. Published in 2021. XanEdu.

Resources and Guides

PAPER STYLE GUIDE FOR COMM 1500

All papers for COMM1500 must follow the guidelines below and seen in the sample paper found at the end of the workbook. Although the style guide roughly follows the American Psychological Association's style guide, there are specific elements for this paper, so do not simply use an online APA source. **If you use an online APA source instead AND it differs from these guidelines, you will lose points on your paper so follow the workbook's guidelines.**

A sample mockup of a paper written in APA style (including a reference page) is found at the end of this section. This sample paper illustrates many of the concepts discussed below and should only be used as a formatting guide.

All COMM1500 papers must:

- ✓ be typed, printed on standard-sized paper (8.5''x11'') and stapled

- ✓ be double-spaced (everything including title page, references, quotations, tables, end notes, EVERYTHING)

- ✓ include 1-inch margins for all four margins

- ✓ use 12 pt. Times New Roman font

- ✓ include a title page that includes the title of the paper, your name, your instructor's name, and the time your class meets

  - o Title should be centered between margins, approximately halfway down the paper

- ✓ provide appropriately formatted **in-text citations** and a **reference page (see below)**

- ✓ not have any **extra spaces** between paragraphs. Under the paragraph option, on the "indents and spacing" page, set "spacing before" and "spacing after" to 0 for the whole text.

APA FAQ

➢ **What should my title look like?**
Titles (like all text in the paper) should be black, Times Roman 12 point font and double spaced. No italicizing, bolding, underlining, color or fancy font.

➢ *Word keeps putting an extra space between my paragraphs. How do I fix this?*
Under the paragraph option, on the "indents and spacing" page, set "spacing before" and "spacing after" to 0 for the whole text. Another way to do this is to Select all text. Under the "Page Layout" tab, select the "Paragraph" option. When the paragraph box pops up, check the box that says "Don't add space between paragraphs of the same style."

➢ *What gets italicized?*
Titles of books, journals, plays, movies and television shows should all be italicized in text. The titles of individual episodes of a TV series should be placed within quotation marks. Key terms or phrases are also italicized.

➢ *How do I cite the COMM1500 Workbook and textbook?*
See the reference page of APA sample paper (found on the last page of this workbook) or see the example references below under "Book without an author" for the workbook and "An edition of a book" for the textbook.

All references and examples were created for this class and constructed in accordance with the APA Style Guide: www.apastyle.apa.org

> ➤ *What should my table look like?* If your class paper requires a table, it must be double spaced, fit within the 1" margins and uses Times Roman 12 point font. An example is shown below:

Table 1. Summary of My Conflict Styles

	Self Ratings	Jake (Best Friend)	Kathy (Mom)	Average score
Competitive	4	4	5	4.33
Collaborating	6	2	3	3.67
Compromising	3	4	4	3.67
Avoidant	7	5	6	6
Accommodating	4	6	5	5

Citations in the Text

To avoid being charged with plagiarism, you must give credit to your sources within your paper. Providing a citation on the reference page is not enough. You will either paraphrase the source or provide a direct quotation from the source within the paper's text.

You can see examples of how to directly quote an author (such as the textbook) and how to cite an author when you are paraphrasing their work in the sample APA paper at the end of the workbook.

> **Paraphrased Text:** To paraphrase means to summarize another's work. **It does not mean to swap out a few words from the original text and present it as your own sentence.** This is considered plagiarism and a violation of UGA's Academic Honesty Code.

> You'll either provide the citation information in parenthesis at the end of the sentence or within the sentence. For example,

> > This research reaffirmed that interpersonal communication competence, as
> >
> > measured, was related to how satisfied people were with their communication (Rubin &
> >
> > Martin, 1994) **OR** The research by Rubin and Martin (1994) reaffirmed that interpersonal
> >
> > communication competence was related to how satisfied people were with their
> >
> > communication.

> When multiple studies support what you have to say, you can include multiple citations inside the same set of parentheses. Alphabetize the studies as they would appear in the reference list and separate them by semicolons:

The research has now shown that interpersonal communication competence is related to

people's satisfaction with their interpersonal communication (Anderson & Martin, 1998;

Rubin & Martin, 1994).

1. **Direct Quotations**: When you directly quote a source in your paper, you provide the source's exact language surrounded by quotation marks. When citing a direct quote, *you must include a page number*. If you have not provided basic source information in the sentence, the direct quotation will be followed by a parenthesis that includes author, date, and a page number. See the following examples:

According to Segal (2007, p. 12), "rhetoric is another word for tendency in language."

Another theorist describes rhetoric as "the use of words by human agents to form attitudes or

to induce actions in other human agents" (Burke, 1969, p. 41).

You should never have a sentence that is only a direct quotation. You should always provide context.

Be sure the direct quotation makes sense in relation to the rest of the paper. For example, the

following is incorrect (but the about examples are acceptable):

"Rhetoric is another word for tendency in language" (Segal, 2007, p. 12).

If an **on-line source** does not include page numbers, you can include any of the following:
- A paragraph number or you can count paragraphs down from the beginning of the document
- An overarching heading plus a paragraph number within that section.
- A short title in quotation marks, in cases in which the heading is too unwieldy to cite in full.

If your **quotation is 40 words or longer**, you will place the information in a block quotation. You should use these sparingly. Again, make sure your paper provides the appropriate context to understand the long quotation. To create a block quotation:
- Omit quotation marks
- Start the quotation on a new line that is indented ½ inch from the left margin
- Follow that formatting with each subsequent line
- Provide the page number outside of the final period

For example:

In *Interpersonal Conflict*, Wilmot and Hocker (2001) argue the following:

One reward for developing a repertoire of conflict styles is that we are then able to see

the behavior of others in a different, more objective light. When we have a wide

repertoire of conflict behaviors, we assume that other people do, too. We are far less

likely to judge the behavior of others automatically as having evil intent, being childish,

or being improper. (pp. 135-136)

2. To **cite a movie or television show** in your text, you cite it in text the same way you would cite an article from a journal or a book. For example, to refer to this episode of the TV show that aired for the first time in 1986:

> Wendy, S. W. (Writer), & Martian, I. R. (Director). (1986). The rising angel and the
>
> falling ape [Television series episode]. In D. Dude (Producer), *Creatures and*
>
> *monsters*. Los Angeles, CA: Belarus Studios.

In the text you would cite Wendy and Martian (1986) or (Wendy & Martian, 1986). For example:

> The myth of the falling ape was an important plot line in the mid-80s (Wendy & Martian,
>
> 1986).

3. To **cite a secondary source** in your text, identify the original authors(s) and publication year of the original source in a signal phrase. Then list the secondary source in your reference list and include the secondary source in parentheses with the page number and using the phrase "as cited in" followed by the properly formatted citation.

> Maslow's (1970) hierarchy of needs helps us explain motives for interpersonal
>
> communication (as cited in McCornack & Morrison, 2019, p. 14).

4. For citations with three or more authors, include the first author's last name followed by "et al." instead of listing all the authors. For example:

> The relational turbulence theory posits that "relational turbulence increases the rigidity of
>
> privacy boundaries between the couple and the social network" (Solomon et al., 2016, p.
>
> 522).

Reference Page

If you cited a source in your paper, it must appear in the reference list. Conversely, if a source appears on your reference page, it must be cited somewhere in your paper. The only exception to this rule is personal communication (emails, personal interviews), which is only cited in the paper and is discussed below.

➤ See the sample reference page at the end of this workbook for an accurate example of how to set up your reference page. It illustrates how the textbook and the workbook should be referenced. It also shows you how to accurately do in-text citations.

➤ *What's wrong with citation machines I find online?* Citation machines are typically inaccurate and will produce incorrect citations and reference page entries. Use the information provided here to manually produce textual citations and your reference page.

➤ Reference pages are:

- o Alphabetized by the first author's **last** name.
- o Doubled-spaced and no addition spaces between entries. See "APA FAQ" if you are having trouble with automatic spacing in Word.

➢ References use hanging indentation: the first line should be flush left, but each additional line of the reference needs to be indented. A hanging indentation command is found by going to the paragraph options. Second, click on the Indents and Spacing. Third, under "Special," click on "Hanging." That command will automatically make your references conform to a hanging indentation. A faster method to handing indents is to highlight the all the references then hit Ctrl+T (Windows) or Command+T (Macs).

➢ Most titles are capitalized like sentences. This means that only the first word or the word that follows a colon is capitalized.

- o The exceptions to this rule are journals and periodicals. Capitalize all major words.

➢ For location, use the city followed by the state's postal abbreviation (i.e., Athens, GA).

➢ Because online URLs can change, the APA recommends utilizing a Digital Object Identifier (DOI) in your references whenever possible. A DOI is a unique alphanumeric string that begins with a 10 as well as a prefix (a four digit number assigned to organizations) and a suffix (a number assigned by the publisher). Many publishers will include the DOI on the first page of an electronic document. If a DOI is available, simply include it at the end of the reference as follows: - https://doi.org10.0000/0000000000)

Reference page formulas and examples: See below for both formulas and sample entries for common types of references. [Author=author's last name, F=author's first initial, M=author's middle initial if applicable]

➢ **An edition of a book**, such as your textbook: Author, F. M. (Year of publication). *Title of work: Capital letter also for subtitle* (number ed.). Publisher.

McCornack, S., & Morrison, K. (2019). *Reflect and relate: An introduction to interpersonal*

communication (5th ed.). Bedford/St. Martin's.

➢ **Book without an author**, such as your workbook: *Title of work: Capital letter also for subtitle.* (Year of publication). Location: Publisher.

COMM1500 workbook. (2021). XanEdu.

➢ **Book**: Author, F. M. (Year of publication). *Title of work: Capital letter also for subtitle.* Publisher.

Segal, J. (2005). *Health and the rhetoric of medicine.* Southern Illinois University Press.

➢ **Book with more than one author**: Author, F. M., Author, F. M., & Author, F. M. (Year of publication). *Title of work: Capital letter also for subtitle.* Publisher.

Orbe, M. & Harris, T. M. (2015). *Interracial communication: Theory to practice* (3rd ed.). Sage

Publications.

➢ **Chapter in a book**: Author, F. M. (Year of publication). Title of chapter or entry. In A. Editor, B. Editor, & C. Editor (Eds.), Title of book (pp. xx-xx). Location: Publisher.

Lannutti, P. J., & Monahan, J. (2009). Social cognition under the influence: Drinking while

communicating. In D. R. Roskos-Ewoldsen & J. L Monahan, J. L. (Eds.),

Communication and social cognition: Theories and methods (pp. 217-244). Routledge.

Parenthetical citation: (Lannutti & Monahan, 2009)

➤ **Journal Article**: Author, F. M. (Year of publication). Title of article. *Title of Journal, Volume number* (Issue number), pp-pp. doi:

Arroyo, A., Segrin, C., Harwood, J., & Bonito, J. A. (2017). Co-rumination of fat talk and weight

control practices: An application of confirmation theory. *Health Communication,*

32, 438-450. doi: 10.1080/10410236.2016.1140263

Parenthetical citation: (Arroyo et al., 2017)

➤ **Journal Article with no DOI**: Author, F. M. (Year of publication). Title of article. *Title of Journal, Volume number* (Issue number), pp-pp. weblink:

Boss, P. (2004). Ambiguous loss research, theory, and practice: Reflections after 9/11. *Journal of*

Marriage and Family, 66, 551-566. www.jstor.org/stable/3600212

➤ **Movie**: Basic reference list format: Director, F. M. (Director). (Year of distribution). *Title of motion picture* [Film]. Studio or distributor.

Smithee, A. F. (Director). (2001). *Really big disaster movie* [Film]. Paramount Pictures.

*Note: If a movie or video tape is not available in wide distribution, add the following to your citation after the country of origin: (Available from Distributor name, full address and zip code).

➤ **TV Show, specific episode:** Writer, W. W. (Writer), & Director, D. D. (Director). (Year of distribution, Month Day). Title of episode (Television series season and episode)[TV series episode]. In P. Producer (Executive Producers), Series title. Production Company.

Oakley, B. (Writer, Weinstein, J. (Writer), & Lynch, J. (Director). (1995, May 21). Who shot Mr.

Burns? (Part one) (Season 6, Episode 25) [TV seriers episode]. In D. Mirkin, J. L.

Brooks, M. Groening, & S. Simon (Executive Producers), The Simpsons. Gracie Films;

Twentieth Century Fox Film Corporation.

➤ **News article online**: Author, F. M. (date of publication) Title of article. Site name. Retrieved from http://home page of source to avoid broken URLs

All references and examples were created for this class and constructed in accordance with the APA Style Guide: www.apastyle.apa.org

Aviv, R. (2007, November 4). Don't be shy. New York Times. Retrieved from

http://www.nytimes.com

➢ **Website**: Author, F. M. (Date of publication). *Title of document*. Retrieved from http://web address

Thompson, S. (2014, January 26). Types of interpersonal conflict. Live Strong.

http://www.livestrong.com/article/133713-types-interpersonal-conflict/

➢ **Electronic entry without a date or author**, such as a dictionary definition: Title of document (n.d.). In Title of source. http://web address

Heuristic. (n.d.). In *Merriam-Webster's online dictionary*. Retrieved from http://www.m-

w.com/dictionary/heuristic.

➢ **Class lecture notes**: Author, A. (date). [Lecture notes on topic] Personal collection of A. Author, school or organization they teach for, city, state.

Schaller, K. (2015, March 3). [Lecture notes on nonverbal communications strategies]. Personal

Collection of K. Schaller, University of Georgia, Athens, GA.

*Note: If the slides come from a classroom website, learning management system (e.g., Canvas, Blackboard), or company intranet and you are writing for an audience with access to that resource, provide the name of the site and its URL

➢ **Class handout**: Author, A. (year). Title of the hand out. [Class handout]. Department, Institution, City, State Abbreviation.

Schaller, K. (2015). Nonverbal Communication Strategies. [Class handout]. Department of

Communication Studies, University of Georgia, Athens, GA.

➢ **Personal communication**: For example, a class discussion, email, or personal interview are all considered personal communication and therefore **not included in your reference list**. However, you will parenthetically cite the communicator's name, the phrase "personal communication," and the date of exchange in your paper. For example:

C. Huggins also said that COMM1500 students tend to be the best and brightest at the University

of Georgia (personal communication, April 12, 2015). Other professors have expressed similar

sentiment about COMM1500 students (K. Schaller, personal communication, April 15, 2015).

See your instructor if you have a source that does not fit into any of the above categories.

All references and examples were created for this class and constructed in accordance with the APA Style Guide: www.apastyle.apa.org

Need help with your writing?

Writing Center. UGA provides a service to help you improve your writing. You can receive free help with writing at the Writing Center. Drop in for tutoring or make an appointment with a writing center consultant.
Bring the assignment description and this style guide with you to the appointment. Be sure the consultant knows you **must follow this style guide.** Visit the Writing Center's website for more information: http://writingcenter.english.uga.edu/

Don't forget about the Library! UGA's library system offers more than just books. If you find yourself needing help at any point during the research and paper writing process, contact a librarian for help!

You can contact a librarian through:
- *Email*: see libs.uga.edu for email webform
- *Telephone*: 706.542.0698
- *Text*: 706.363.0836
- *Online chat*: libs.uga.edu
- *In person*: Reference desks located:
    - Main Library
    - Science Library
    - MLC
    - Curriculum Materials Library

Using PowerPoint to Enhance a Presentation

As a student, you've likely sat through many PowerPoint presentations. However, frequent viewing of PowerPoint slides does not necessarily correlate with the ability to create an effective PowerPoint presentation. The way an instructor uses a PowerPoint presentation to teach a concept is different from the way you will use PowerPoint in your group presentation. If you are planning to use PowerPoint, consider the following guidelines and tips.

General Guidelines for PowerPoint: PowerPoint can be a smart addition to your presentation if it is used effectively. Keep the following guidelines in mind:
- Use colors, fonts, and slide design to engage, not distract, your audience. *Simplicity is key* when creating a PowerPoint to accompany your presentation.
- Use a PowerPoint slide to
    - *make a point more interesting*
    - *when you need help communicating complex information*
    - *when you want to improve the audience's comprehension and retention of an idea, or to advance an argument.*
- Test-drive your slideshow. Have the entire group try out the talk in a dress rehearsal with the slides. Work out the kinks before the presentation.
- When practicing the group presentation, include your PowerPoint slideshow each time.

Common PowerPoint Mistakes: As you are crafting your presentation, work to avoid these common mistakes:
- **Too much content**: Some people put everything they hope to say on their PowerPoint slides. This is no longer a visual aid, but instead, your outline and will result in a poor grade! Even though a PowerPoint presentation that is loaded with content might be helpful for you when you are copying down notes during lecture, it is not a good presentation. If you put your entire presentation on a visual, your audience will likely read your visual instead of listening to you speak. Remember to keep your PowerPoint *visual*, not verbal.

- **Too little preparation**: It is easy to spot a group who has not practiced with PowerPoint or is not familiar enough with the software. The following are examples of students who were ill-prepared to use PowerPoint:
    - Forgetting to talk about some slides
    - Exiting out of the presentation before the presentation is over
    - Failing to embed video and images correctly. If you are not familiar with how to embed video and images, visit the resources listed on the next page.

- **Confusing layout**: The design options for your PowerPoint presentation are nearly endless. However, some groups choose layouts and designs that make it difficult for audience members to decipher the content. Avoid the following mistakes:
    - Do not use light colored fonts that do not stand out on the screen.
    - Do not choose complex backgrounds that compete with the purpose of the slide
    - Do not capitalizing all words or format the font in ways that are off-putting to audience members.

- **Distraction**: Audience members are easily distracted. Use the "Animations" command to show only the point you are presently talking about. Don't put on the screen more than one point at a time as the audience will read what is on the screen rather than listen to you.

Bad Example:

Good Example:

Need help creating your PowerPoint presentation?

You can access free written and video PowerPoint tutorials on Microsoft Office's support page:

http://office.microsoft.com/en-us/support/

OR

Log-on to Lynda.com, which has a variety of software tutorials for all experience levels. Go the following site and follow the instructions:

http://eits.uga.edu/learning_and_training/lynda

Sample Presentation Outline

Fill in all of the components <u>in complete sentences. Avoid using more than one sentence per point.</u>

Note: *Information in the brackets (e.g., [First sub-topic]) is a description of what needs to be included in that point of the outline. The brackets should **NOT** be included in the final version of the outline.*

This sample is for formatting purposes only. The content of your outline will vary depending on the assignment instructions for your specific section of COMM1500. The purpose of this outline is to provide frame of reference for formatting procedure.

Used by permission of group members: Rachel Saville Snyder, Abigail Leigh Spencer, & Jaclyn Susanne Lee (Lattner)

Native Hawaiian Co-Culture Outline

Introduction

Although part of the United States, the islands that make up Hawaii have a separate and unique culture within the American culture. The culture of Hawaii is very diverse and is influenced by a number of ancient cultures including Portuguese and Mexican. This blend of cultures is expressed in the language, food, art, and traditions of the native Hawaiian people. At the center of the culture is the idea of the "Aloha Spirit", which is the "coordination of mind and heart within each person" (Hawaiian Culture & History). By studying the communication behavior of native Hawaiians, it is clear that the culture is a blend of many others but stands out with its unique traditions and language.

Body

I.   [The first sub-topic] Greeting and goodbye behaviors

    A.   [First supporting information for the sub-topic] Hawaiians greet one another with a kiss on the cheek (Hawaiian Culture & History).

B.   [Second supporting information for the sub-topic] If you are invited into someone's house, remove your shoes before entering (Beal, 2013).

C.   [Third supporting information for the sub-topic] Always accept a lei when it is offered to you.

        1.   [Detail of the information] Wear it for the whole event.

        i.   [Detail of the information] Do not take off the lei in front of the person who gave it to you (Beal, 2013).

II.   [The second sub-topic] Language

A.   [First supporting information for the sub-topic] "The long history of immigration and ethnic diversity brought a mixture of languages" (Headley & Kaniho, 2018)

        1.   [Detail of the information] Influenced by: Japanese, Portuguese, English, Chinese, Korean, Filipino

B.   [Second supporting information for the sub-topic] Pidgi is the local dialect of Hawaii (Beal, 2013)

C.   [Third supporting information for the sub-topic] Examples of slang (Headley, & Kaniho, 2018)

        1.   [Detail of the information] Aloha = hello, goodbye, love, affection

        2.   [Detail of the information] Ainokea = I don't care

        3.   [Detail of the information] Choke = to have a lot of something

        4.   [Detail of the information] Kapu = forbidden, taboo

D.   [Fourth supporting information for the sub-topic] Written Hawaiian language - based on English letters (Hawaiian standardized)

   1.   [Detail of the information] Eight consonants (h, k, l, m, n, p, w)

   2.   [Detail of the information] Five vowels (a, e, i, o, u)

E.   [Fifth supporting information for the sub-topic] Rules of the language

   1.   "Hawaiian words will never end with a consonant" (Cook)

   2.   "Syllables in Hawaiian words are only one or two letter and must end with a vowel" (Cook)

III.   [The third sub-topic] Nonverbal cues

A.   [First supporting information for the sub-topic] Physical Appearance

   1.   [Detail of the information] Tattoos ("Nonverbal Cues")

      a)   [Addition detail of the information] Hawaiian tattoos reflect Hawaiian heritage and cultural identity through symbols.

   2.   [Detail of the information] Leis ("Hawaiian Lei Etiquette", 2017)

      a)   [Addition detail of the information] A special gift signifying friendship and celebration.

      b)   [Additional detail of the information] It is considered rude and disrespectful to remove a lei in the presence of the person who gave it to you.

B.   [Second supporting information for the sub-topic] Polychronic ("Monochronic and Polychronic Cultures" 2015)

   1.   [Detail of the information] Hawaiians have a loose and relaxed sense of time this is best observed in their use of Haole vs Hawaiian time.

      a)   [Additional detail of the information] Haole time: used to express the exact time. Haole is a word associated with non-native Hawaiians.

      b)   [Additional detail of the information] Hawaiian time: used to express general time.

C.   [Third supporting information for the sub-topic] Haptics (Anthony, 1979)

   1.   [Detail of the information] Body Contact

      a)   [Additional detail of the information] Touch is used to signal affection or friendship and is not limited to immediate family members and friends.

      b)   [Additional detail of the information] Includes punching, slapping, pinching for attention or to make a point.

   2.   [Detail of the information] Honi "the English translation is "to kiss", but actually, the original greeting was touching forehead to forehead, nose to nose and exchanging breath" (Naluai, 2019).

   3.   [Detail of the information] Inappropriate to touch the head of an individual unless by parents or older relatives.

      a)   [Additional detail of the information] Western behavior of patting children on the head is considered a physical violation

Conclusion

The native Hawaiian co-culture is heavily influenced by a lot of other countries' cultures. As for language, the Hawaiian people have their own unique alphabet which is shown in their distinct words and phrases. Nonverbal cues convey the value Hawaiians place on respect and their heritage to express the cultural identity. The people of Hawaii express themselves based on their gender and their roles in society. The co-culture as a whole is collectivistic, meaning they focus on group goals and wellness rather than individual members. In conclusion, Hawaiian culture is distinct in its value of traditions and community within verbal and nonverbal communication.

References

Anthony, Alberta P. "Hawaiian Nonverbal Communication: Two Classroom

Applications." ERIC, March 31, 1979.

https://kumuchunswebsite.weebly.com/uploads/1/3/2/2/13222998/non_verbal_commu

nic ation.pdf. (Student name)

Beal, S. (2013, January 3). Minding Your Manners in Hawaii. Retrieved from

https://www.govisithawaii.com/2007/08/20/minding-your-manners-in-hawaii/.

(Student name)

Cook, D. Hawaiian Language Basics. Retrieved from

http://www.instanthawaii.com/cgi- bin/hawaii?Language. (Student name)

Hawaiian Culture & History. (2019, October 25). Retrieved from

https://www.gohawaii.com/hawaiian-culture. (Student name)

Hawaiian Lei Etiquette. (2017, November 27). Retrieved from

https://traveltoparadise.com/hawaiian-lei-etiquette/. (Student name)

Hawaiian standardized as a written language. Retrieved from

http://www.hawaiihistory.org/index.cfm?fuseaction=ig.page&PageID=280.   (Student name)

Headley, L., & Kaniho, P. (2018, September 19). Say What? Here's the Most Popular

Hawaiian Slang. Retrieved from https://andyoucreations.com/blog/say-what-heres-

the-most- popular-hawaiian-slang/. (Student name)

Naluai, J. (2019, October 4). Honi the Traditional Hawaiian Greeting. Retrieved from

https://www.hoomanaspamaui.com/honi-the-traditional-hawaiian-greeting/.

(Student name)

Nonverbal Cues. (2014, April 29). Retrieved from

https://communication272spring2014.wordpress.com/samoa-hawaii/nonverbal-

cues/. (Student name)

Sample Paper for Formatting
based on Style Guide

Finding Strength in Weakness: Navigating Gaslighting's Challenges to Intimacy Power

Lee M. Pierce

Department of Communication, University of Georgia

COMM1500: Interpersonal Communication

Dr. Jennifer Monahan

March 16, 2021

Finding Strength in Weakness: Navigating Gaslighting's Challenges to Intimacy Power

We all have influence in the world and that influence is a result of our *power currency* or the particular means by which people achieve objectives. U.S. culture often limits "valid" power currencies that emphasize punishment and status. Yet a select few have great success with *intimacy* power or influence gained through positive social and emotional rewards. The individualistic culture of the United States, however, offers challenges to intimacy power displays. One of these challenges is —a communication tactic intended to make intimacy-powered individuals feel crazy, abusive, out-of-touch, selfish, etc. (Gass & Nichols, 1988). I argue that gaslighting is effective because it is a tactic that promotes undermining self-doubts while simultaneously appearing as an effect of intimacy power itself. Therefore, I suggest that may neutralize gaslighting without sacrificing empathy. In this essay, I first explain the cultural limitations on intimacy currency, then describe the specific ways gaslighting undermines intimacy currency, and finally illustrate gaslighting through a personal example.

Intimacy power is an effective way to achieve a goal if communicators are patient, withhold judgment, and practice. Empathy is a two-step process combining taking another's perspective and validate their feelings and communicating that concern and validation (McCornack & Morrison, 2019). As an empathetic person, I work hard to communicate with other people in ways that contribute to mutual understanding. For example, my best friend Maude told me last week she was upset because her parents did not give her the rose gold watch she wanted for her birthday. After listening to her emote for a while I asked, "What specifically makes you so upset about not getting the watch?" Maude replied, "I don't know." "Maybe you don't feel like your parents listen to you?" I asked encouragingly. "Or maybe you felt like you deserved something nice after all of your hard work this semester," I added. After our back and forth to fine-tune her perspective, Maude finally explained, "I guess I just thought if they really believed how much I've matured they'd buy me something really nice that I could take care of and would look professional on me." With that information I expressed empathetic concern, "I really feel for you. This transition to adulthood feels like such a struggle sometimes and I can understand how important validation is to you." Maude put her head on my shoulder, indicating she felt understood and validated. We grew closer as friends and I honed my skills as an empathetic communicator, which will serve me well in utilizing intimacy power to achieve future objectives.

The Limitations of Intimacy Power

Despite the benefits noted above, intimacy power and the empathy on which it depends are often dismissed in U.S. culture as weakness or powerlessness. McCornack & Morrison (2019, p. 251) explains that, "People are granted power according to the degree to which those power currencies are valued in a given culture." Therefore, someone may possess potentially effective intimacy power but not achieve much influence because of cultural perceptions of empathetic behaviors as non-powerful or weak. Under these conditions, for example, Maude's emotions surrounding the birthday gift would have been perceived as childish, selfish, or weak; in an individualistic culture, Maude would be responsible for her own disappointment and expected to get over the disappointment or never experience it in the first place. Had I shared those expectations, I would not have been able to offer the empathetic perspective taking that led to my increased intimacy power and our enhanced relationship.

Unfortunately, the individualistic values in U.S. culture often fail to appreciate the strengths of a more community-focused intimacy power (Pierce, 2015). By now it is hopefully obvious that intimacy power effectively achieves relationship goals but it is also extremely effective in more instrumental or "practical" goals. In other words, when we associate intimacy power only with relationship building we miss the point that seriously engaging multiple perspectives, especially when they compete with our own, increases our ability to achieve any kind of goal. Zaki (2012) explains that perspective taking plays in important role in everything from Israeli-Palestinian conflict to student-mentor disagreements to negotiating the purchase of a new car. Perspective taking can also make all the difference when delivering terrifying news or a negative diagnosis in the medical field (Dalhousie University, n.d.) Although putting my assumptions about Maude on hold was difficult, doing so allowed me to see the problem in its complexity rather than oversimplifying it. However, it is exactly this insightful ability that often threatens more culturally established forms of power.

Understanding and Neutralizing Gaslighting

Surprisingly, individuals accustomed to achieving goals using more coercive or status-oriented forms of power are especially threatened by displays of intimacy power (COMM1500 Workbook, 2019). Typically, overt power users are more comfortable engaging similarly oriented individuals. This preference stems from and reinforces the very lack of perspective taking that is a unique skill of the intimacy-powered individual. For example, as a coercive or punishment-powered person, my friend Maude confronted her parents about the disappointing birthday by saying, "if we can't listen to each other about our needs then we may as well just forget about holidays all together." While Maude greatly appreciated the empathy that I provided as an intimacy-powered individual, she is unable to effectively utilize that power currency to get her needs met in ways that are not coercive or legitimate. Part of the problem is that she hasn't honed the necessary skills but the other part is that she has embraced the cultural expectations for dominating power displays. When coercive or status-powered individuals such as Maude must engage in conflict with an intimacy-powered person, what happens?

When overtly dominating power styles feel threatened by intimacy power they often switch gears to engage in an emotionally undermining tactic known as gaslighting. Dorpat (2007) defines gaslighting as any covert attempt to "undermine the other person's confidence in [his or her] emotional reactions and [his or her] own perception of reality" (p. 180). As opposed to threats, hostility, or commands, covert tactics such as gaslighting are more disarming and can often be mistaken for empathy to an undiscerning ear. Gaslighting as a covert tactic is seen displayed in the movie *Gaslighting* (Hornblow & Cukor, 1944). Although it has similar effects on the victim, gaslighting can often fly under the abuse radar, subtly and seriously damaging its victims. For example, last time Maude and I disagreed it took me several weeks to understand I was being gaslighted. I asked her to pick me up from the airport and when she arrived four hours late, we had the following conversation:

Maude: Ugh. Sorry I'm so late. I totally got caught in traffic. How was the flight?

Me: Long. I appreciate you picking me up really if it's inconvenient you should let me know. All I want to do after a long trip is get home. I would have scheduled the shuttle.

Maude: I said I was sorry! I'm sorry you don't like your free ride from the airport.

Me: I absolutely appreciate you. I want both of us to be happy and I know that shuttling to the airport is a pain. I just want to be clear that I'm happy to take the shuttle.

Maude: You never told me I had to be perfectly on time to the second. It's normal to hit traffic going to the airport. Are you always on time when you go someplace?

Me: No. Traffic is a nightmare, which is why I don't want to stress us out to save $35. So next time, if I ask, be honest if you don't want to take me, okay?

Maude: You're right. I'm the worst. I can't even be on time. I'm a terrible friend.

I was made to feel guilty and unjustified for asking Maude to be on time by the conversation.

Following the conversation I felt guilty and unjustified for asking Maude to be on time. I spent

the next few weeks being extra nice to her even though I was the one who had been stood up at

the airport. Maude she used gaslighting tactics to turn the tables quickly. In her second line

above she used her usual coercive tactic: hostile joking. When I didn't respond to her liking and

pursued my objective, she turned to "crazy making" in her third line, delegitimizing my

perception of events and drawing on my own self-doubt to undermine me (Gass & Nichols,

1988). She effectively silenced me in her fourth line, punishing herself and effectively

activating my empathetic hardwiring. What should an empathetic individual such as myself do

against such effective tactic?

The temptation may be to fight fire with fire but intimacy-powered individuals are better

off drawing on and replenishing their power currency—positive emotional and social rewards—

by deploying I-feel statements. I-feel statements allow the speaker to overtly call out the

gaslighter on their behavior without giving in to a temptation to strike back (Gass & Nichols,

1988). To capitalize on the power of the I-feel statement, speakers should explain directly how

the gaslighting is making them feel and end with a collaborative statement. For example, if I

were to re-do my conflict with Maude above, I would have paused after her last statement and

said, "Maude, I'm feeling crazy and frustrated what I perceive as a reasonable request is coming

across as unreasonable to you. How can we resolve this?" If Maude is as good a friend as I think

she is, knowing that her response is affecting me this way should be enough for her to reflect on

her behavior. If not, then it at least provides me an empathetic strategy for continuing to assert

my needs. In the end, if I-feel statements don't draw the gaslighter's attention to their own unethical behavior it may be time to re-evaluate the relationship. Careful, sensitive, and generous, intimacy-powered individuals deserve to share their strength with those who can appreciate and help cultivate it.

Although many power currencies are available to communicators, culture plays a determining role in which currencies are perceived as legitimate and have effects. As this essay has demonstrated, cultures that over-emphasize self-reliance, individuality and displays of aggression can miss out on the strengths that intimacy-powered individuals offer: social support, emotional understanding, and grace. Once of the ways these strengths are regularly undermined is through gaslighting, a communicative behavior that utilizes crazy-making, excessive guilt, and delegitimizing perspectives to undermine the communitarian objectives of intimacy-powered individuals. I-feel statements are an invaluable resource for empathetic individuals wishing to neutralize gaslighting without resorting to the toxic behaviors of coercion, punishment, and domination. However, as with all relationships, the ultimately strength is the ability to let go of toxic and ultimately it is intimacy-powered people who always have the strength to forgive, forget, and forge new relationships.

References

COMM 1500 workbook: Introduction to interpersonal communication (2019). XanEdu.

Dalhousie University Faculty of Medicine Communication Skills Program (n.d.). Expressing

    empathy to patients. http://csp.medicine.dal.ca/docs/Expressing- Empathy.pdf

Dorpat, T. L. (2007). *Crimes of punishment: America's culture of violence.*   Algora Publishing.

Gass, G. Z., & Nichols, W. C. (1988). Gaslighting: A marital syndrome. *Contemporary Family*

    Therapy, *10*, 3-16. https://doi.org/10.1007/BF00922429

Hornblower, A. (Producer), & Cukor, G. (Director). (1944). *Gaslighting* [Motion picture].

    United States: Metro-Goldwyn-Mayer.

McCornack, S., & Morrison, K. (2019). *Reflect and relate: An introduction to interpersonal*

    communication (5th ed.). Bedford/St. Martin's.

Pierce, L. (2015). *Intimacy and Power*. Personal Collection of L. Pierce, University of Georgia,

    Athens, GA.

Zacki, J. (2012, June 11). Sympathy can boost conflict as well as curb it. *Huffington Post.*

    http://www.huffingtonpost.com